Instructional Fair's *Geometry–Grade 4* is a different way for children to learn about geometry. This book focuses on experimenting with shapes and spatial relationships, not just on learning the names of shapes. While doing puzzles and completing patterns, children are developing problem-solving and organizing skills.

Geometry has often been neglected in elementary schools, but recently many educators have been recommending much more geometry content. They believe geometry is useful in a variety of ways in life and that it can also be another context for teaching children problem solving, logic, organizing, and other thinking skills.

Children will differ in their home experiences with geometry and in their innate ability to understand spatial relationships. Some children will have played with puzzles and blocks at home. Others will have had few such experiences. Some children will have a head start on others simply because seeing shapes is something at which they are inherently good. Interestingly enough, children who are good with numbers are not necessarily good with shapes, and children who have trouble with the abstract nature of numbers may find shapes much more concrete and understandable.

As you use the pages in this book with your students, you will find some students will do well on their own, and others will need extra help. Having children work with partners helps. Sharing and discussing the students' results as a class can also help. You may need to try some of the puzzles ahead of time or along with your students.

The geometric skills in this book are grouped by type of activity. The activities are presented in order of difficulty, but their difficulty will vary from child to child. The book is divided into sections, starting with math facts involving shapes and then offering activities on finding shapes, drawing shapes, shading shapes, puzzles with cutout pieces, making designs, patterns, coloring designs, hidden shapes, folding patterns and folding puzzles. The directions on the pages may need to be read aloud and discussed. A glimpse at the answer key may help you better understand the intent of a page. (Note: When children are asked to "shade" a shape, they should use a pencil.) Some children may need help with the cutting and folding.

*Geometry–Grade 4* should be motivating and exciting for children. Rather than using the pages all together as a unit, you might want to consider using one or two a week throughout the year as a change of pace from arithmetic. However you use them, you will find yourself enjoying them right along with your students!

# Hidden Sums

Name_____

- Find each shape with the correct sum.
- Copy the numbers under the sum. The first one is done for you.

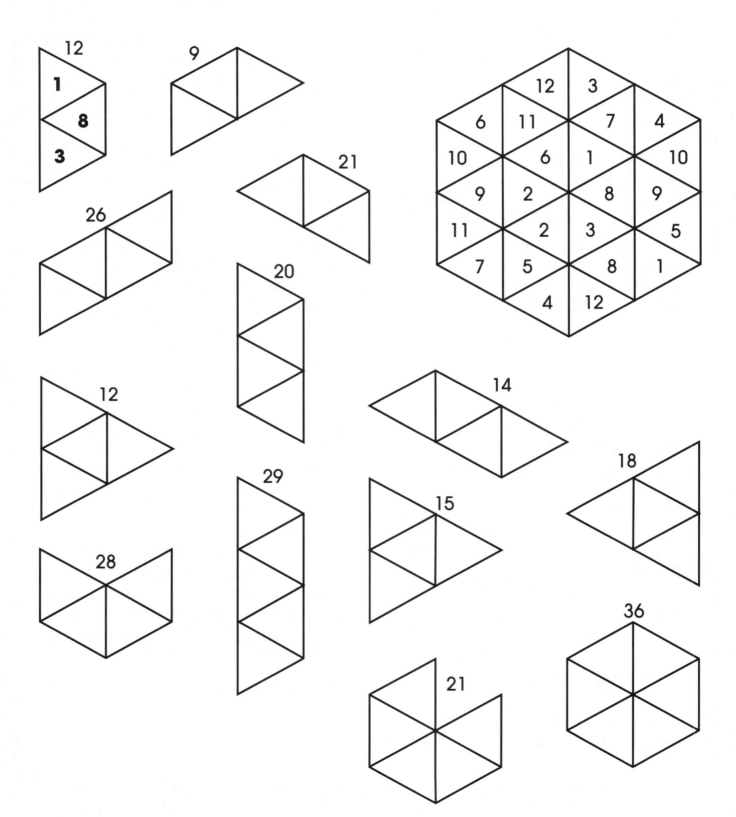

# More Hidden Sums

Name_____

♦ Find each shape with the correct sum.
♦ Copy the numbers under the sum. The first one is done for you.

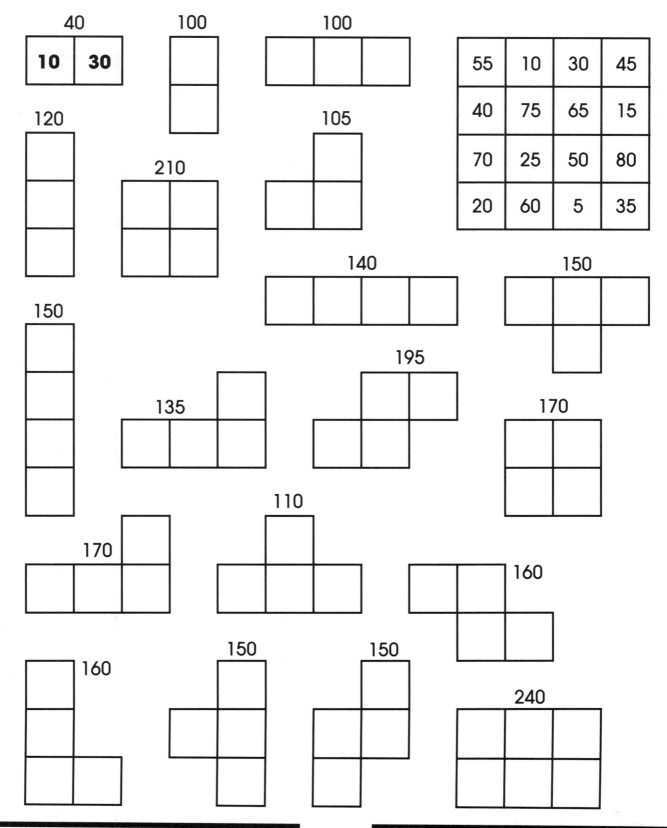

# Hidden Differences

Name_____

♦ Find each shape with the correct difference.
♦ Copy the numbers under the difference. The first one is done for you.

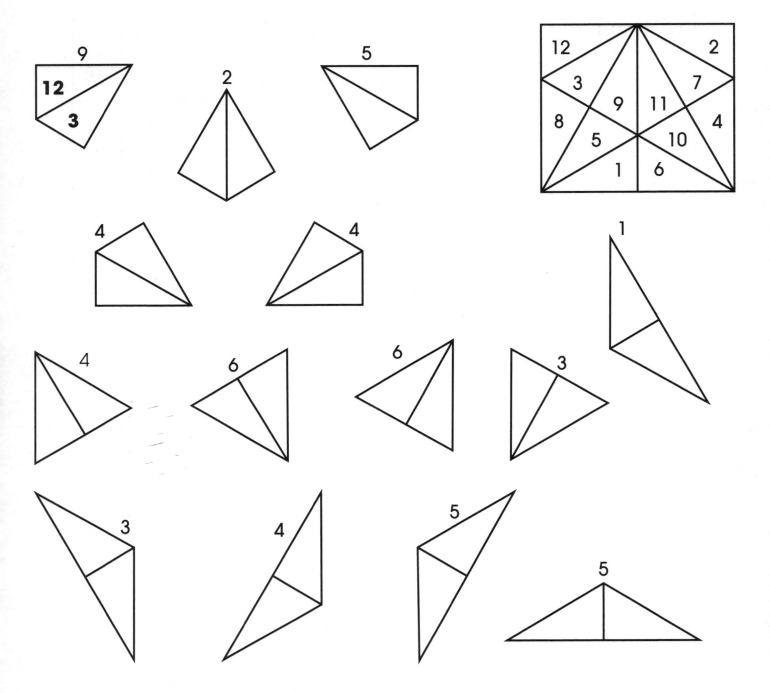

# Hidden Products

Name_____

♦ Find each shape with the correct product.
♦ Copy the numbers under the product. The first one is done for you.

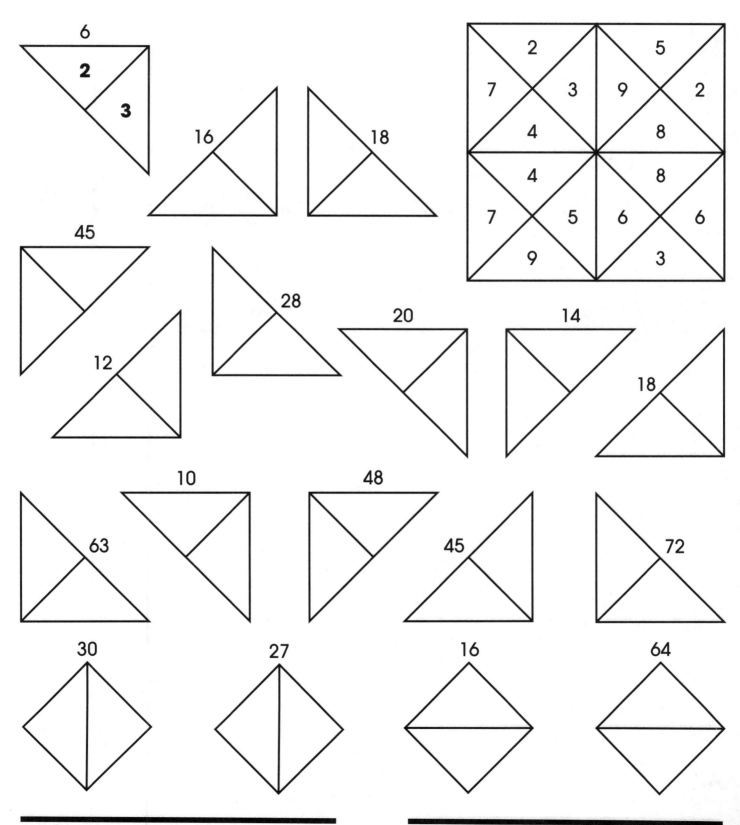

IF5128 Geometry Grade 4

# Hidden Shapes

Name _____

♦ Find Shape 1 in Design 1 and shade it. Do this for each shape. The shape may be turned, but it must be the same size.

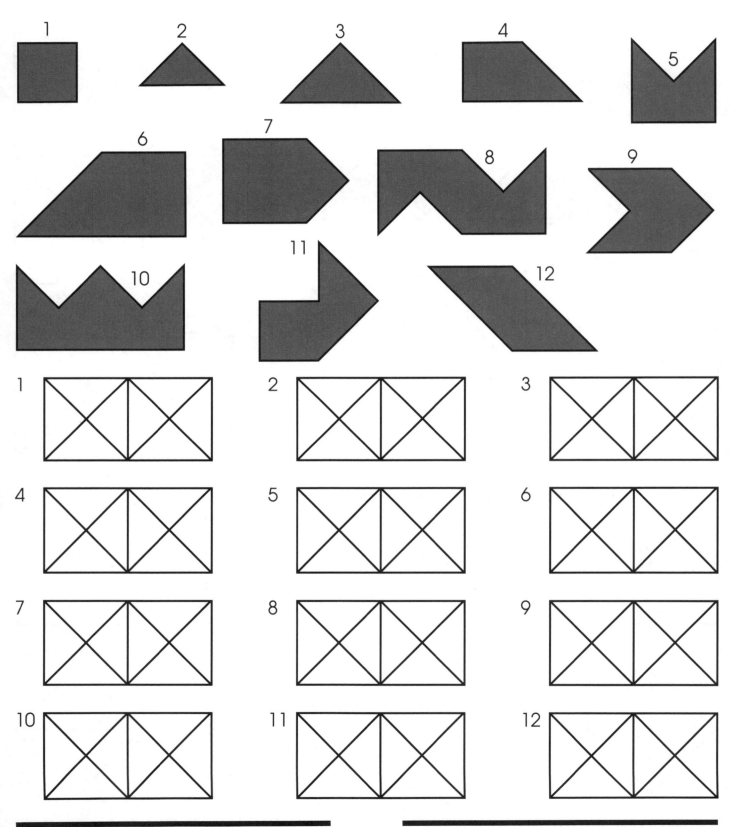

# Figure Finding

Name_____

♦ Find Figure 1 in Design 1 and shade it.  Do this for each shape.
  The figure may be turned, but it must be the same size.

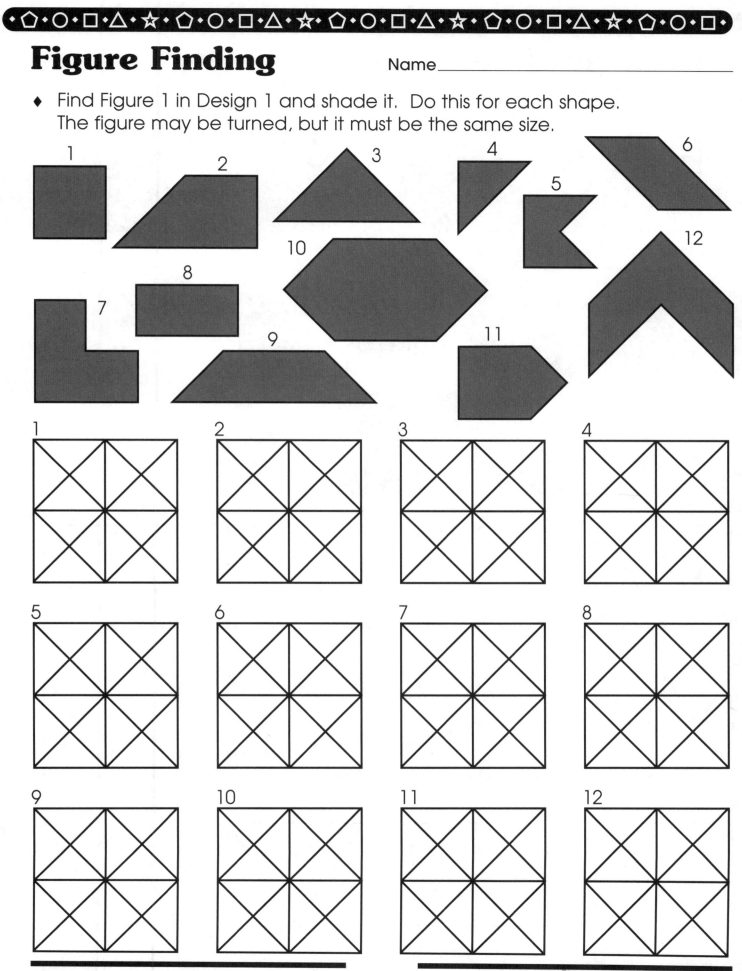

# Camouflaged Shapes

Name_____

♦ Find Shape 1 in Design 1 and shade it. Do this for each shape. The shape may be turned, but it must be the same size.

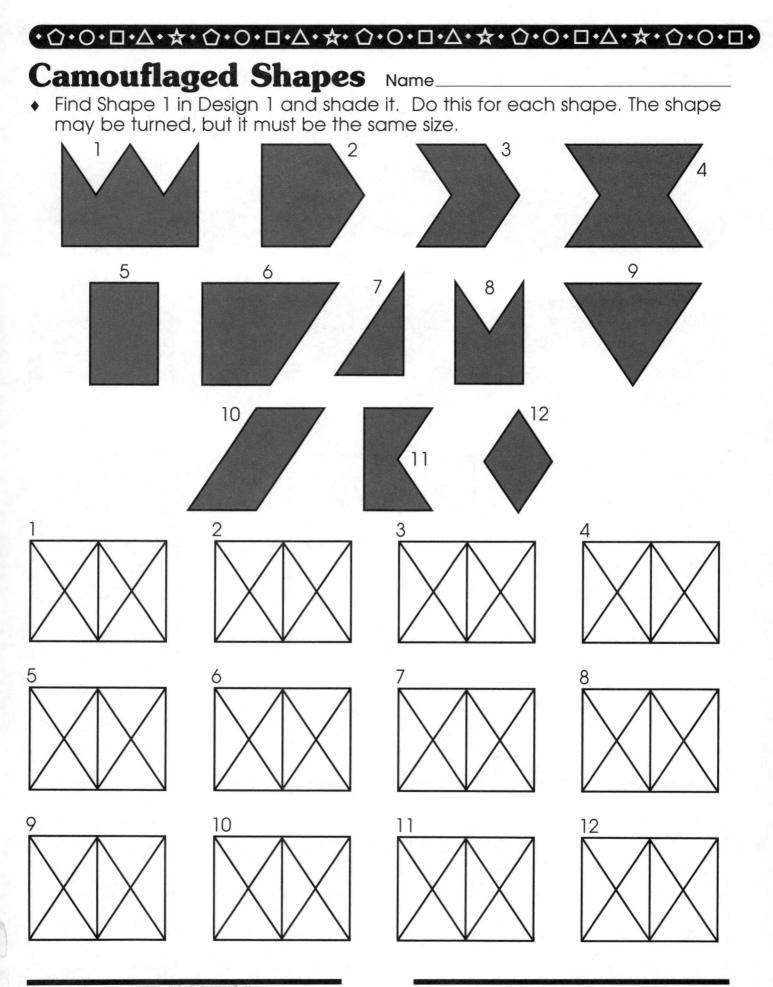

# Fish in Hiding

Name_____

- ♦ All these fish are hiding below.
- ♦ Find them and shade them.

# Squares and Rectangles

♦ Connect dots in each set.
♦ Make a different square or rectangle in each set.

# Dot Search

Name_____

♦ Connect dots to make each shape.

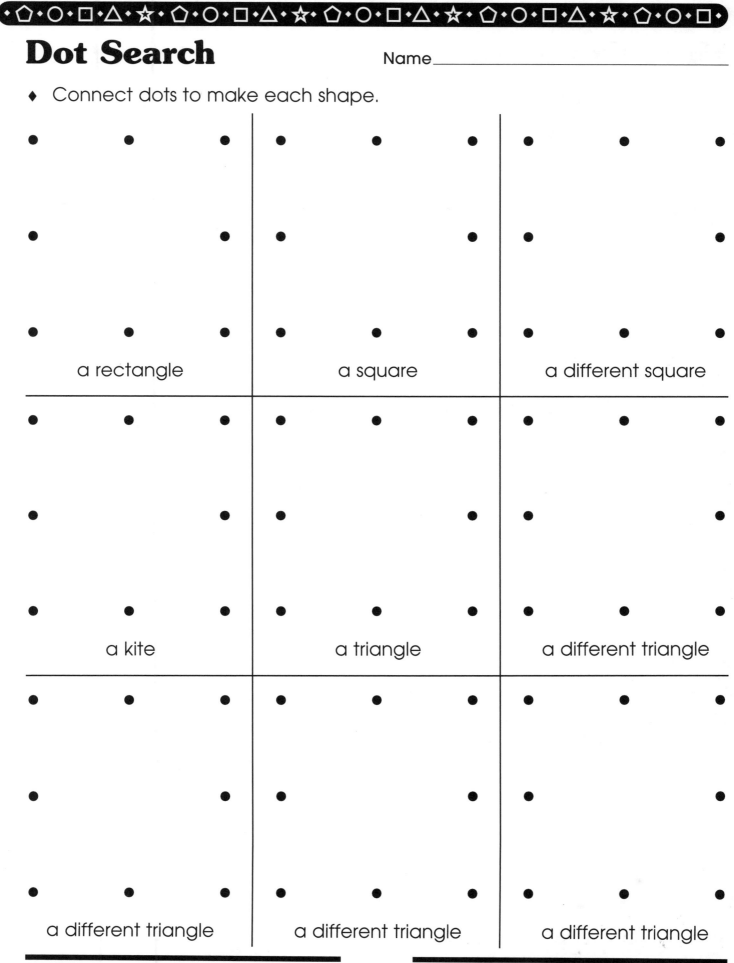

a rectangle | a square | a different square

a kite | a triangle | a different triangle

a different triangle | a different triangle | a different triangle

IF5128 Geometry Grade 4

# More Dot Search

Name_____

♦ Connect dots to make each shape.

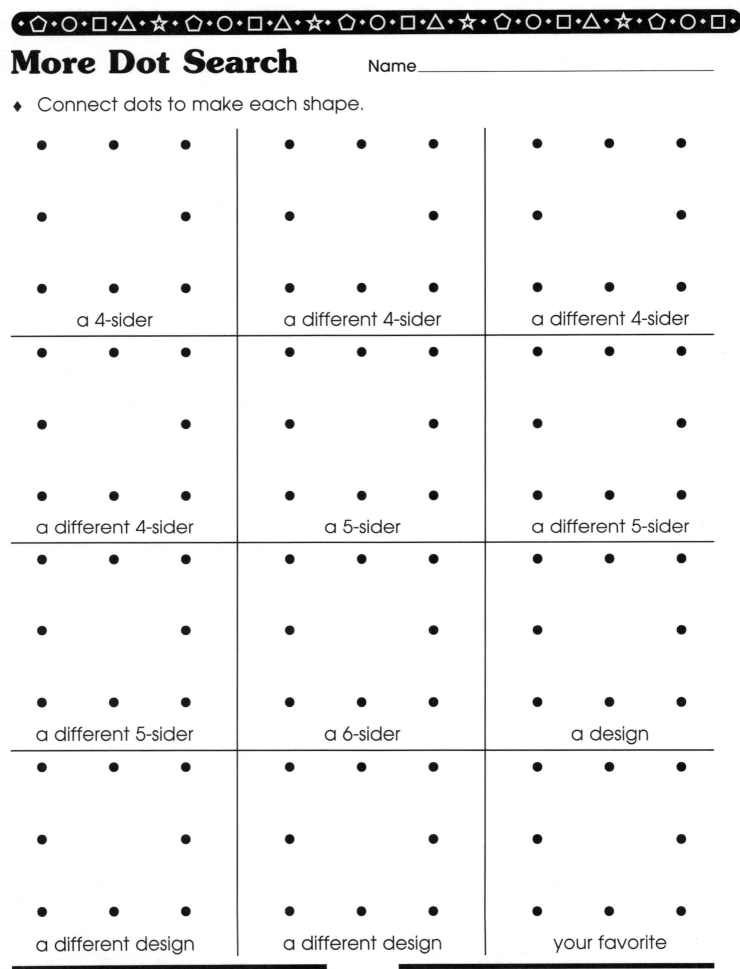

a 4-sider

a different 4-sider

a different 4-sider

a different 4-sider

a 5-sider

a different 5-sider

a different 5-sider

a 6-sider

a design

a different design

a different design

your favorite

# Inside Shapes

Name_____

♦ Connect dots on each circle to make each shape.

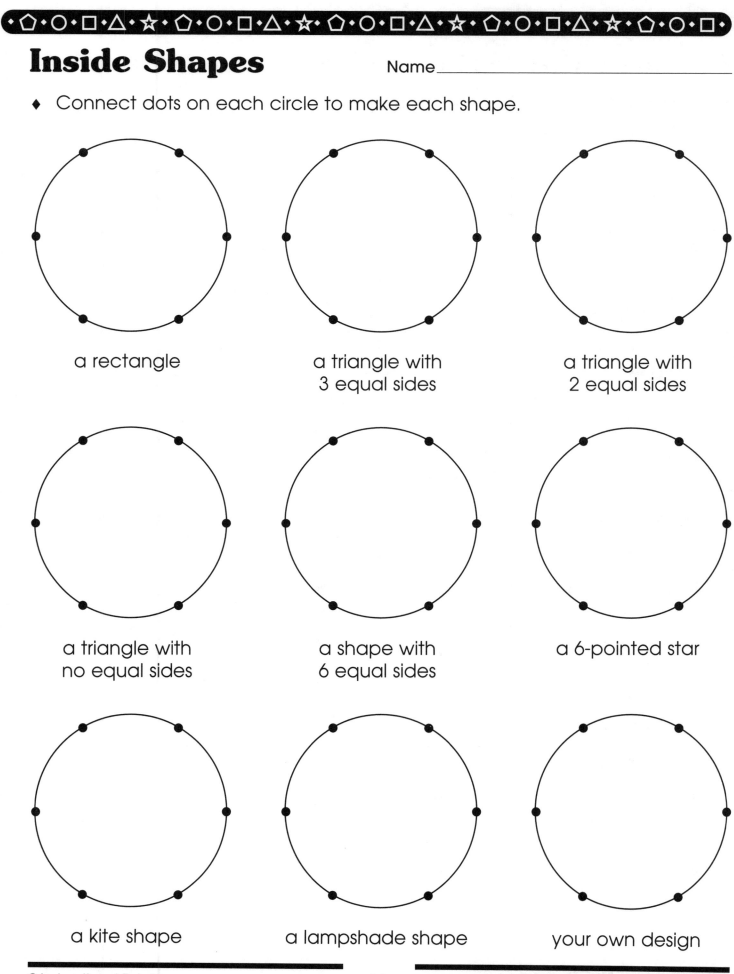

a rectangle

a triangle with
3 equal sides

a triangle with
2 equal sides

a triangle with
no equal sides

a shape with
6 equal sides

a 6-pointed star

a kite shape

a lampshade shape

your own design

# Connect the Dots

Name_____

♦ Connect the dots to make each shape.

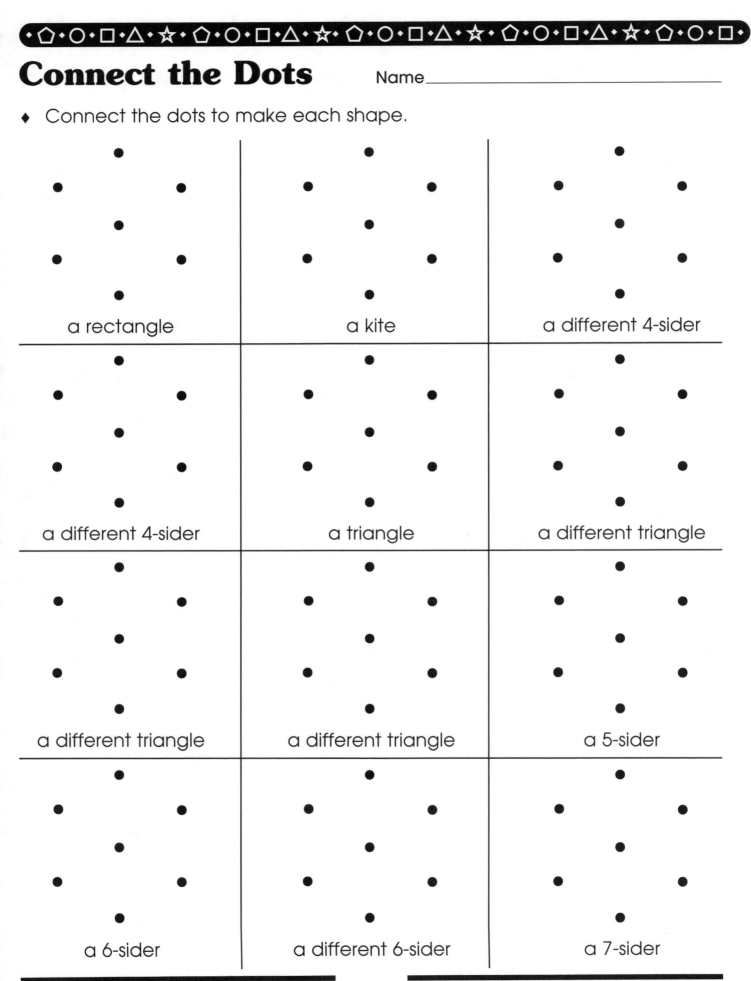

a rectangle

a kite

a different 4-sider

a different 4-sider

a triangle

a different triangle

a different triangle

a different triangle

a 5-sider

a 6-sider

a different 6-sider

a 7-sider

# Shapes in Hiding

Name_____

♦ Shade triangles to make each shape.

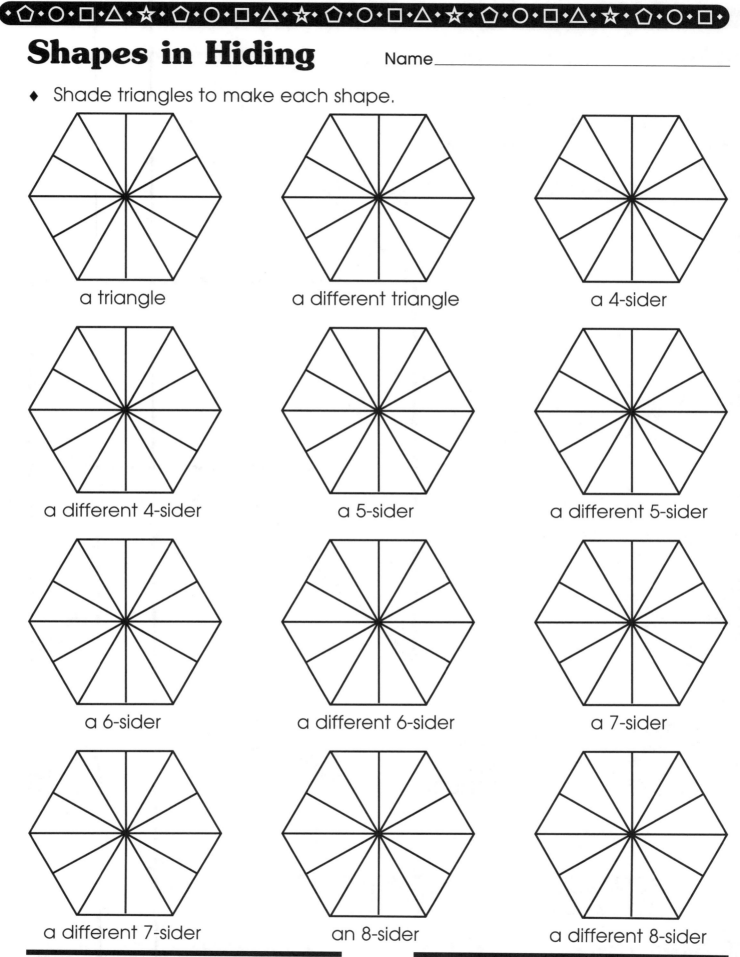

a triangle

a different triangle

a 4-sider

a different 4-sider

a 5-sider

a different 5-sider

a 6-sider

a different 6-sider

a 7-sider

a different 7-sider

an 8-sider

a different 8-sider

15

IF5128 Geometry Grade 4

# The Rocket Puzzle

Name_____

- The rocket has 4 parts.
  Cut them apart.
- The rocket can change itself into many shapes.
- Use all 4 pieces to make each shape below.

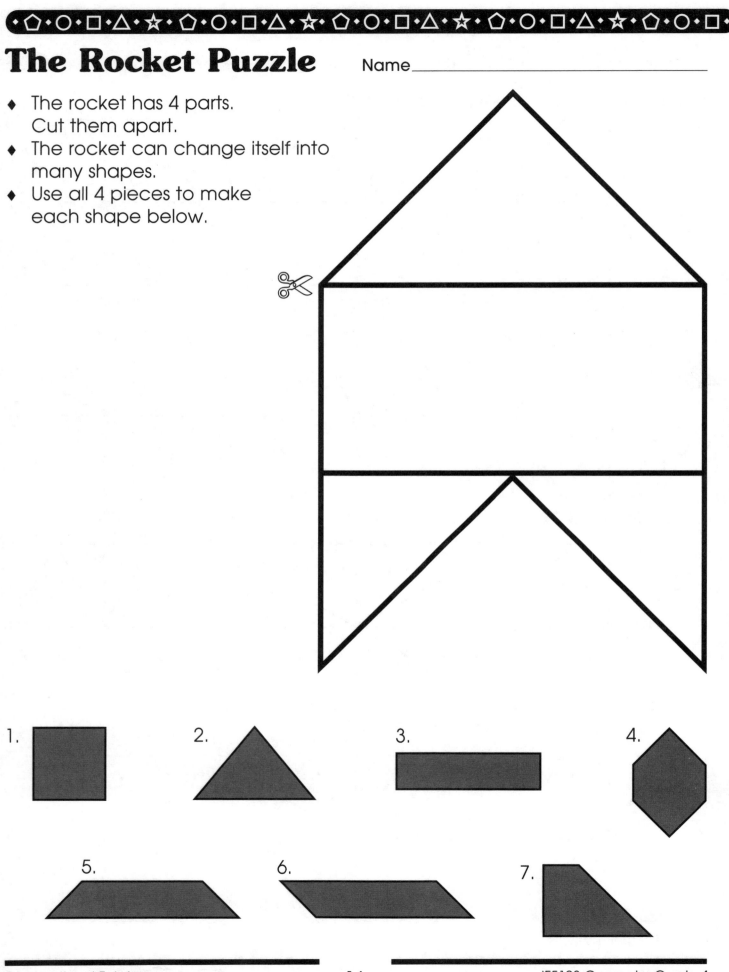

1.

2.

3.

4.

5.

6.

7.

 IF5128 Geometry Grade 4

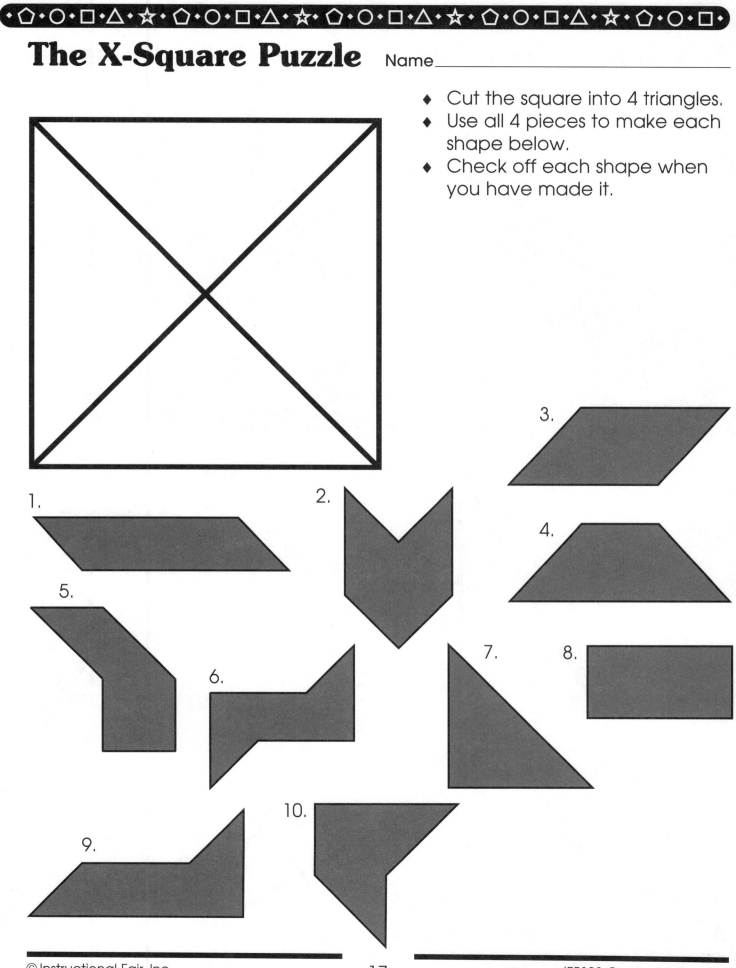

# The X-Square Puzzle

Name _____

- Cut the square into 4 triangles.
- Use all 4 pieces to make each shape below.
- Check off each shape when you have made it.

1.

2.

3.

4.

5.

6.

7.

8.

9.

10.

# 3 Triangle Puzzle

Name_____

◆ Cut out the 3 triangles below.
◆ Use all 3 triangles to make each shape below.

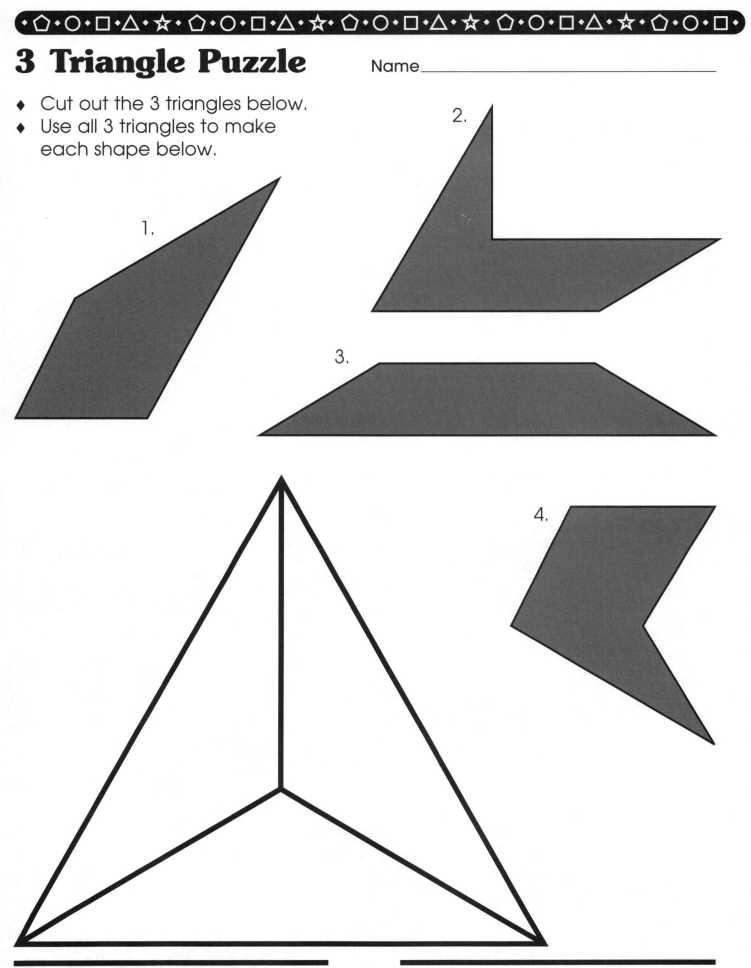

1.

2.

3.

4.

# Another Rocket Puzzle

Name_____

- ♦ This rocket has 4 parts.  Cut them apart.
  It can change itself into many shapes.
- ♦ Use all 4 pieces to make each shape.

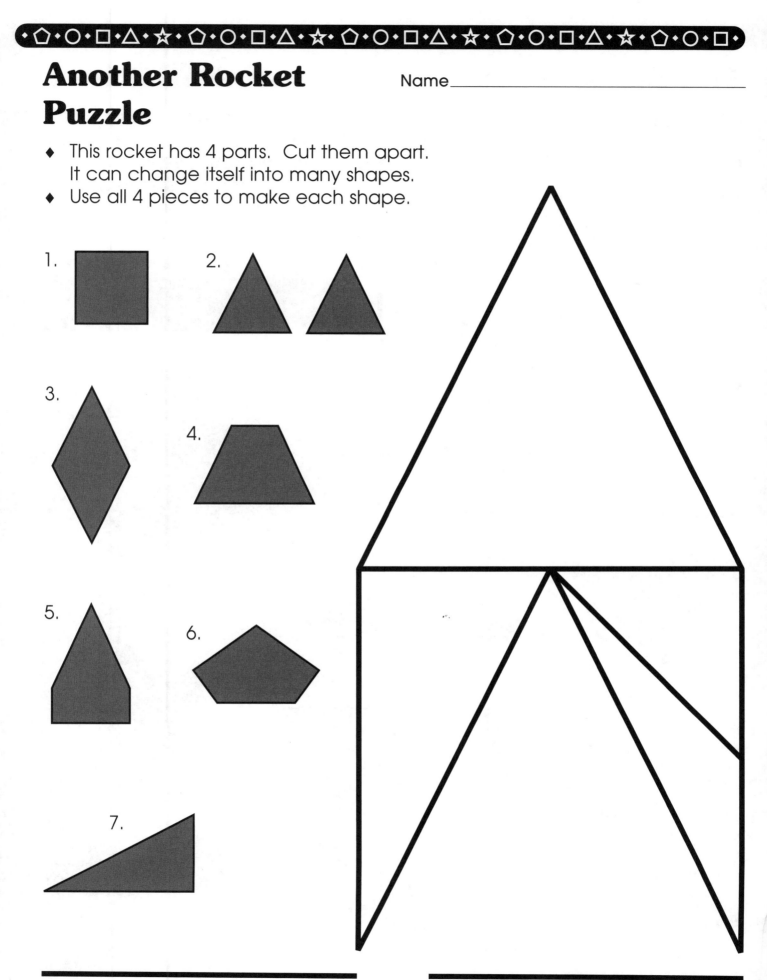

1.

2.

3.

4.

5.

6.

7.

IF5128 Geometry Grade 4

# The Super Square Puzzle

Name_____

- ◆ Cut apart the 3 pieces.
- ◆ Use all 3 pieces to make each shape below.
- ◆ Check off each shape when you have made it.

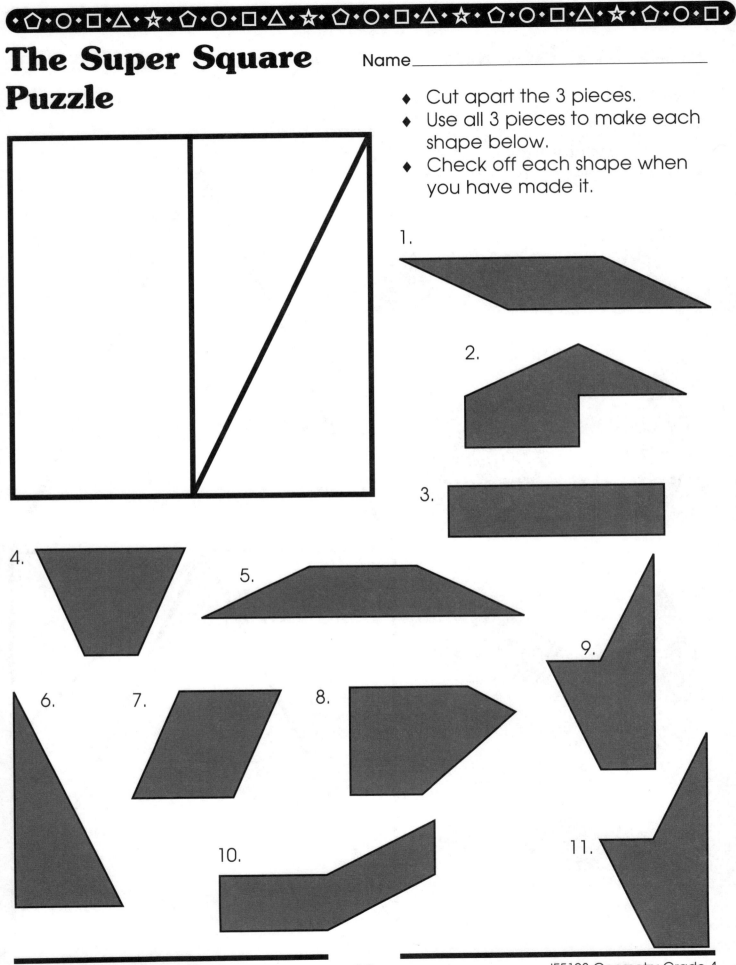

1.

2.

3.

4.

5.

6.

7.

8.

9.

10.

11.

20

IF5128 Geometry Grade 4

# Criss-Cross Designs

Name_____

♦ Shade triangles in each design to make a different shape.

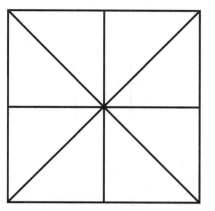 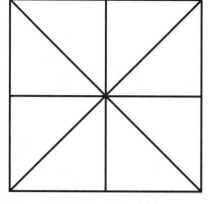 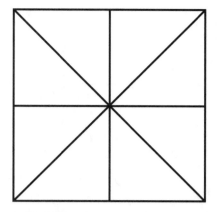

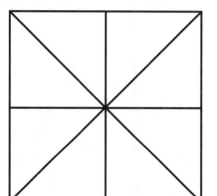 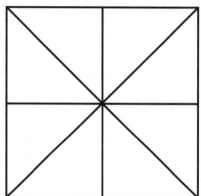 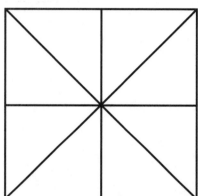

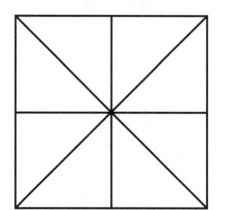 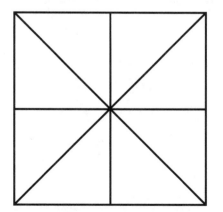 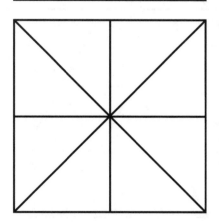

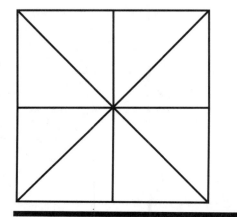 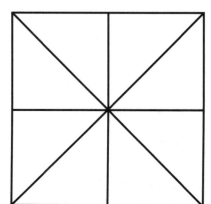 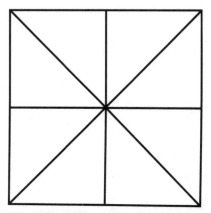

IF5128 Geometry Grade 4

# Triangle Designs

Name_____

◆ Shade triangles in each design to make a different shape.

# Triangle Patterns

Name_____

◆ Shade to keep each pattern going.

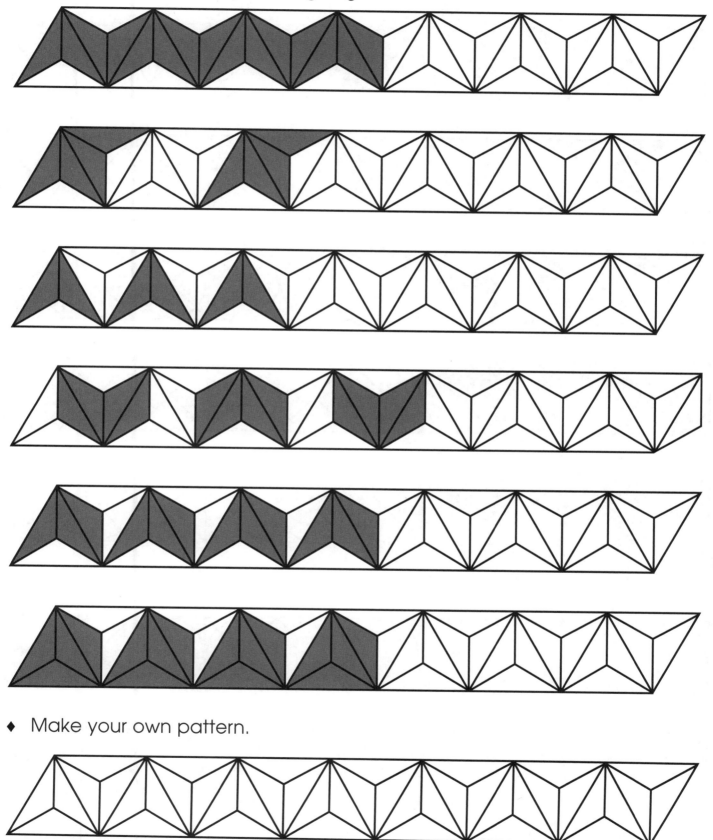

◆ Make your own pattern.

23

# Circles and Squares

Name_____

♦ Shade to keep each pattern going.

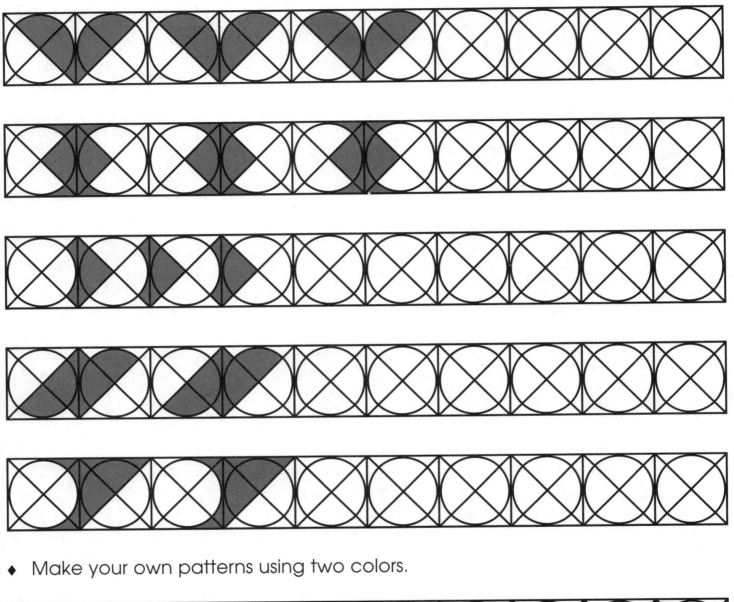

♦ Make your own patterns using two colors.

# Square Patterns

Name_____

♦ Color or shade each rectangular shape in a different pattern.

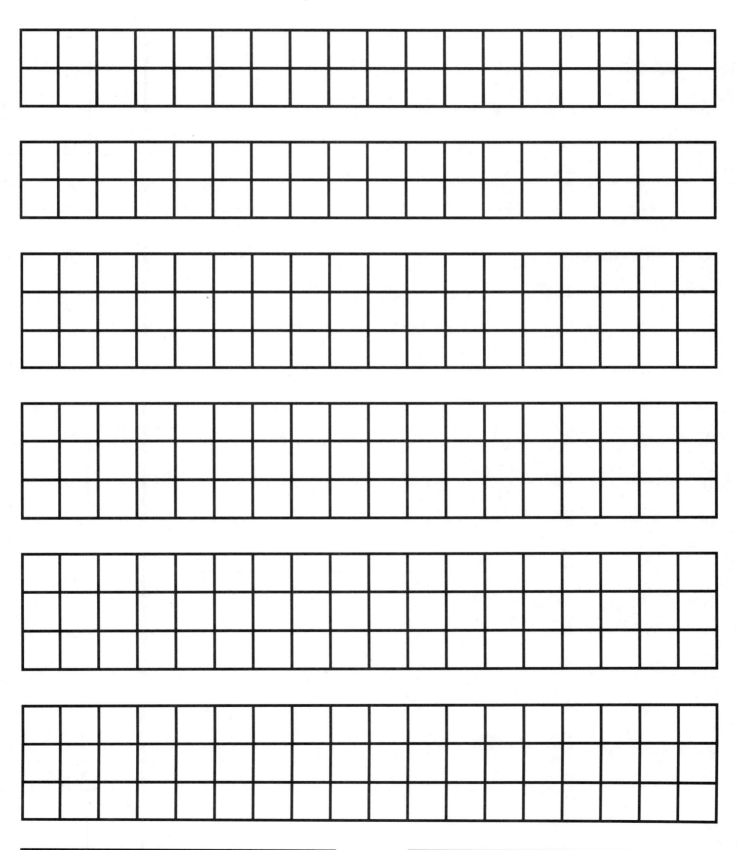

# Wallpaper Patterns

Name_____

◆ Shade to keep each wallpaper pattern going.

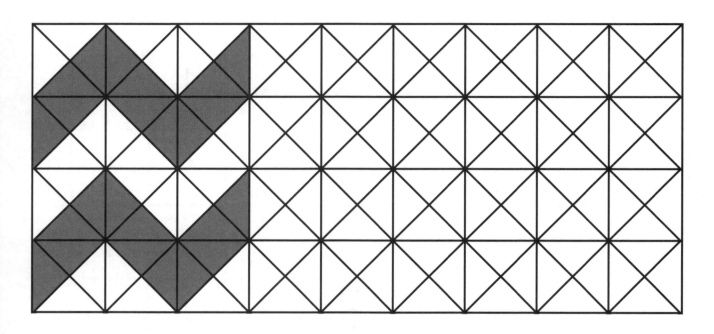

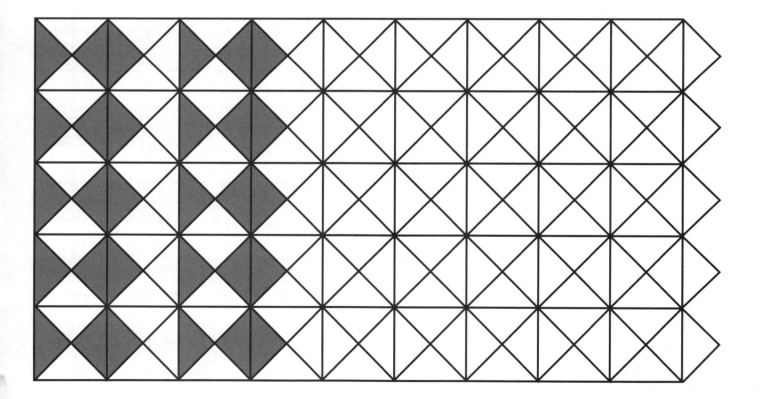

# Dancing Squares

Name_____

- ◆ Pick a color. Color one shape. Then color all the other shapes that are the same size with the same color.
- ◆ Pick a different color. Color another set of shapes.
- ◆ Repeat until all are colored.

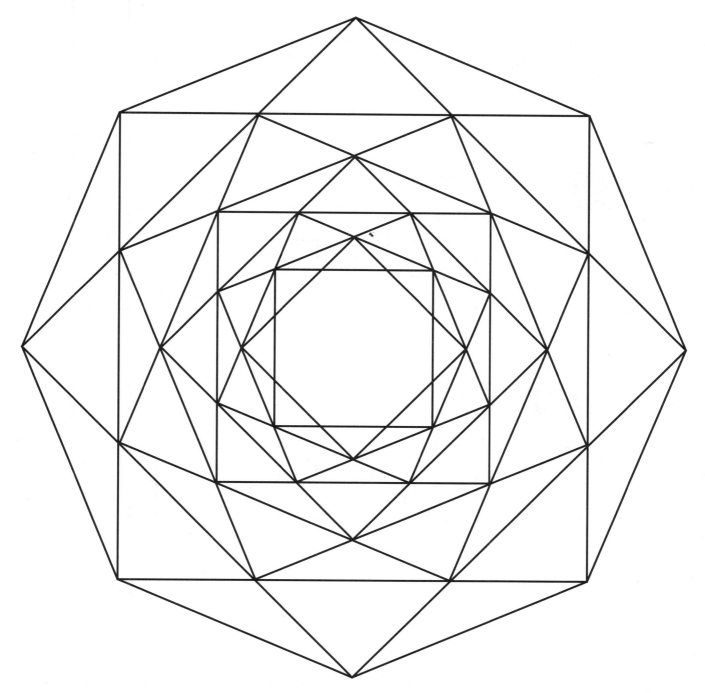

- ◆ Use another copy of this design.
- ◆ Color it a different way.

# Hidden Shapes

Name_____

♦ Hidden in this shape ⊞ are many others.

♦ Find and shade them in copies of the shape.
The shapes may be turned different ways.

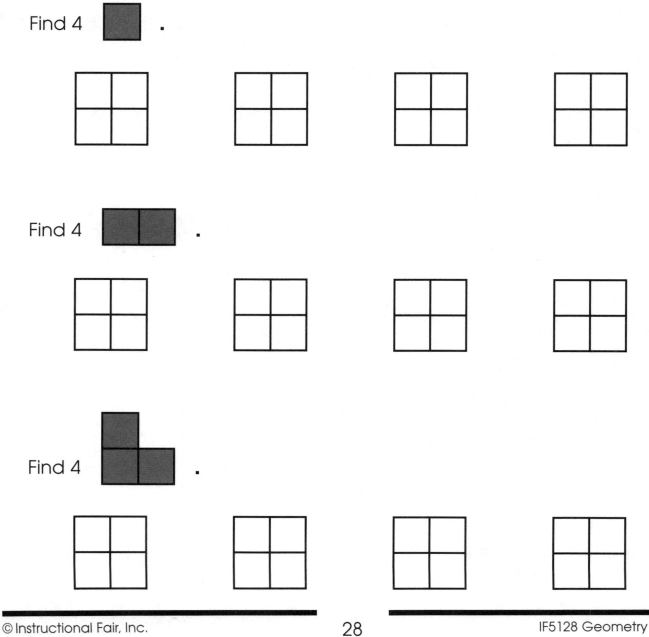

Find 4 ◼ .

Find 4 ▮▮ .

Find 4 .

# More Hidden Shapes  Name_____

♦ Hidden in this shape [diagram] are many others.

♦ Find and shade them in copies of the shape.
   The shapes may be turned different ways or flipped.

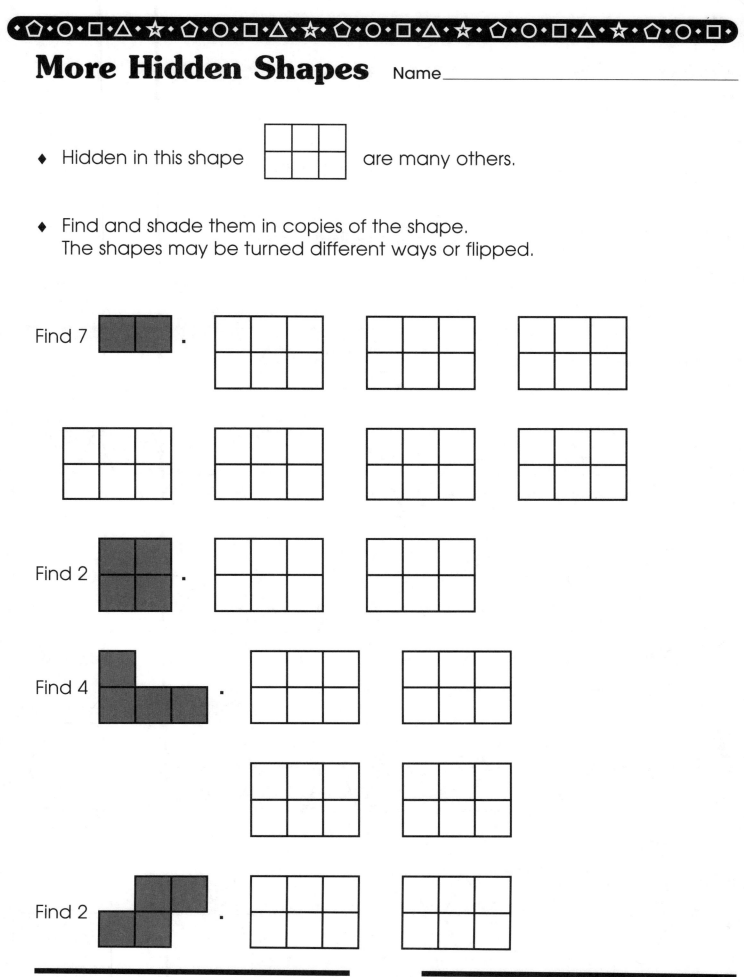

# Hidden Shapes with Triangles

Name_____

- ♦ Hidden in this shape  are many others.

- ♦ Find and shade them in copies of the shape.
  The shapes may be turned different ways.

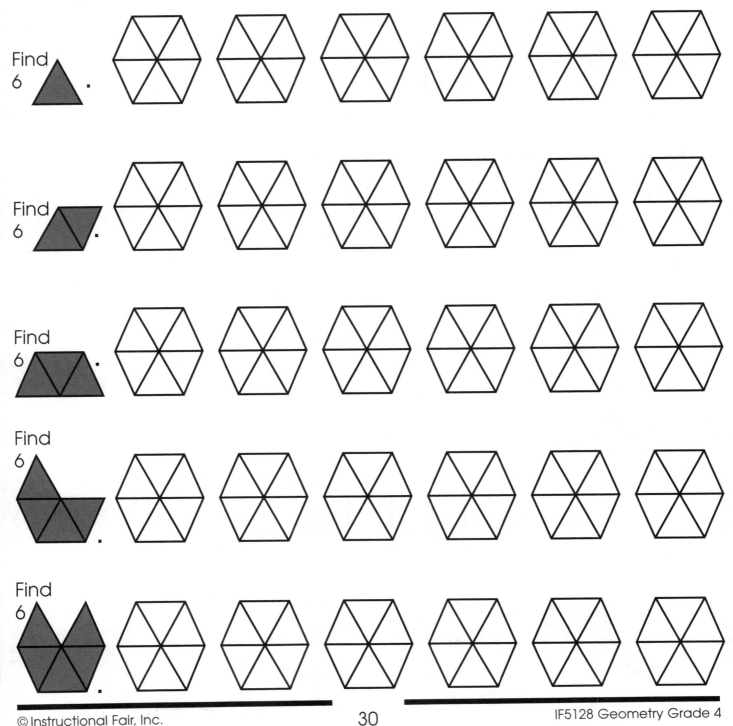

Find 6 ◭.

Find 6 ▱.

Find 6 ⬯.

Find 6

Find 6

# More Hidden Shapes with Triangles

Name_____

♦ Hidden in this shape     are many others.

♦ Find and shade them in copies of the shape.
The shapes may be turned different ways or flipped.

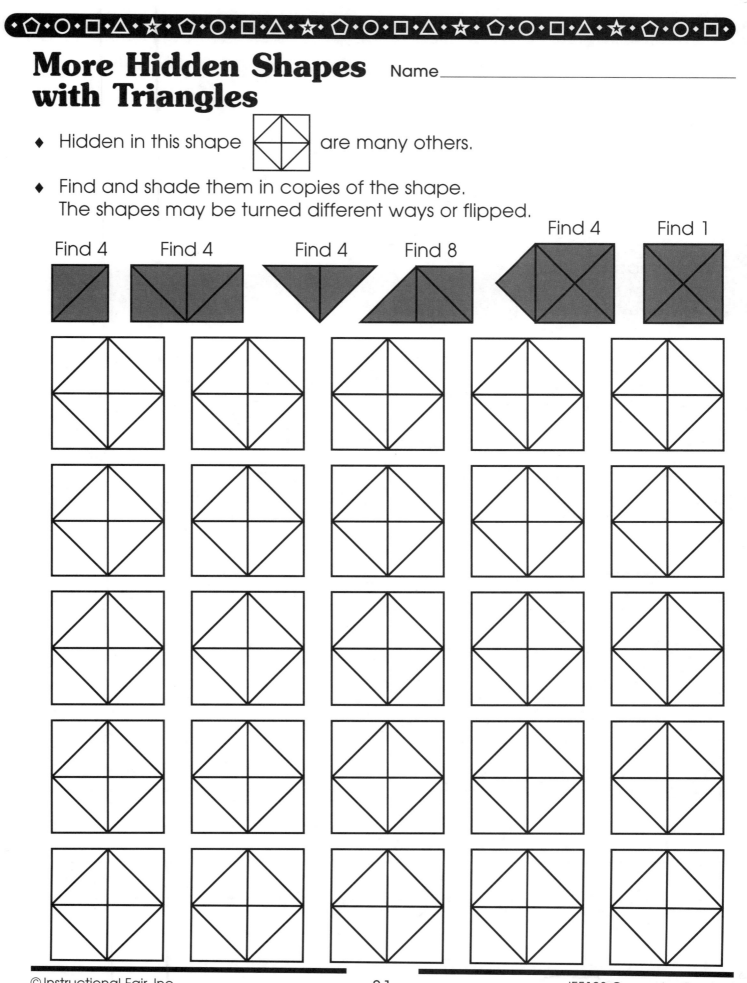

# Triangle Shapes

Name_____

- Shade in shapes made of 4 triangles.
- There are 3 different ones.
  Being turned a different way does not make a shape different.

For example: 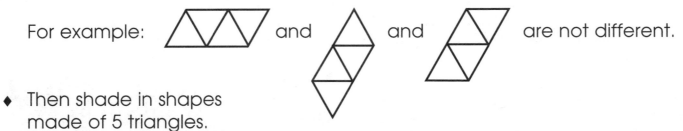 and and are not different.

- Then shade in shapes
  made of 5 triangles.
- There are 4 different ones.

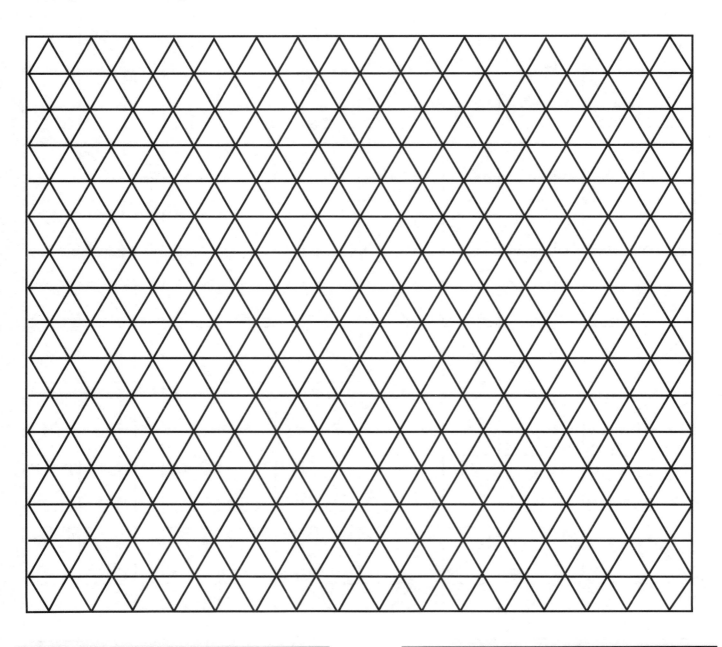

# More Triangle Shapes    Name_____

- ◆ Shade in shapes made of 6 triangles.
- ◆ There are 12 different ones.
  Being turned a different way or flipped does not make a shape different.
- ◆ You may need another copy of the triangle design below.

# Folding Patterns

Name_____

♦ Shade to copy each pattern from the left side to the right side.
♦ If you fold on the dark line the pattern should match.

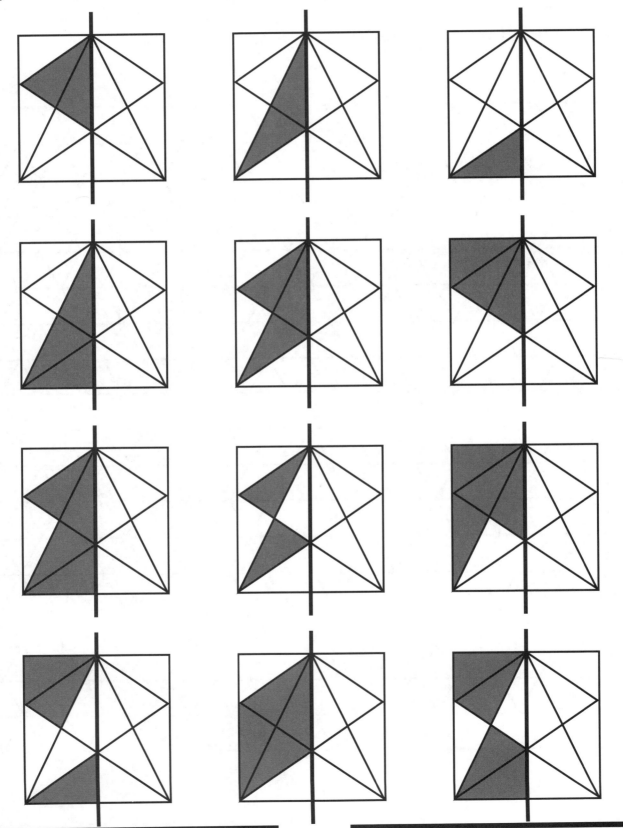

# More Folding Patterns  Name_____

♦ Shade to copy each pattern from the left side to the right side.
♦ If you fold on the dark line the pattern should match.

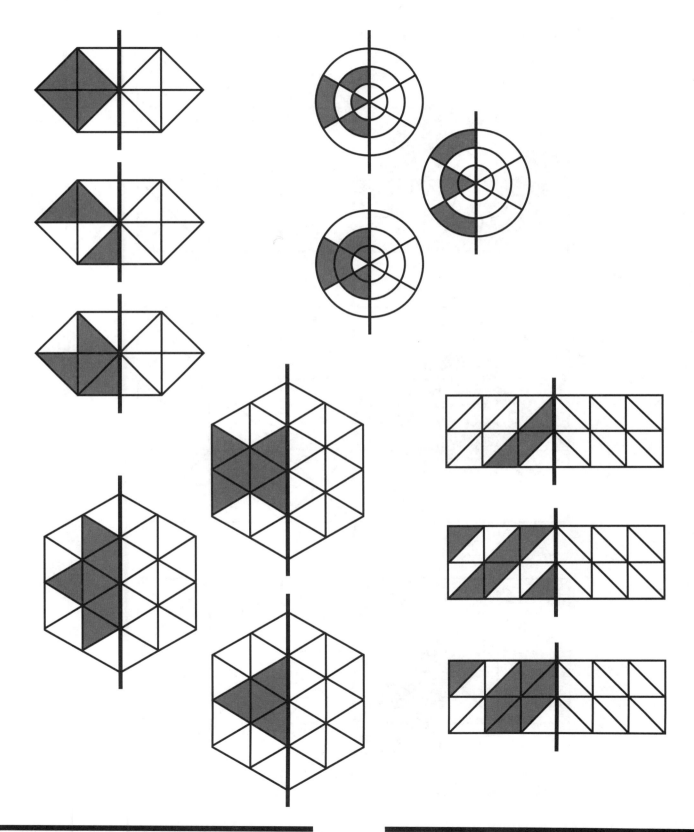

# Large Folding Patterns   Name

◆ Shade to copy each pattern from the left side to the right side.
◆ If you fold on the dark line the pattern should match.

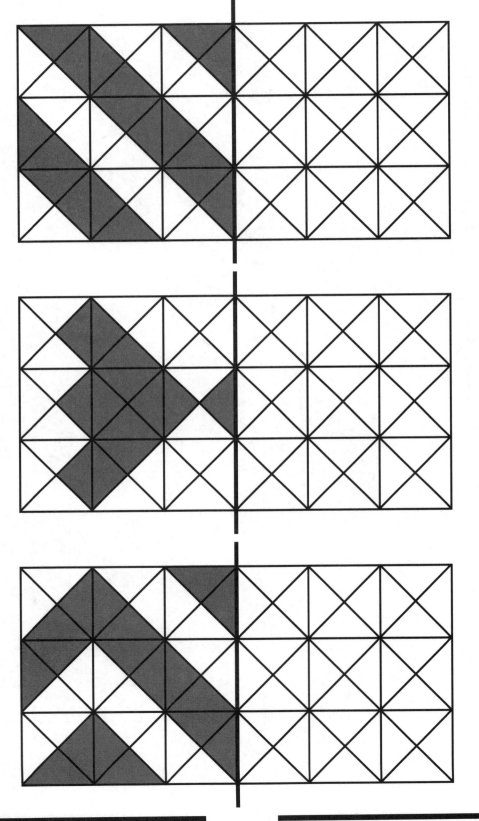

# 9 Triangles Puzzle

Name_____

- These triangles can be folded into all of the shapes below.
- Cut out the large triangle. Fold on each dashed line.
  Trace the fold lines on the back.
- Fold flat to make each shape below.

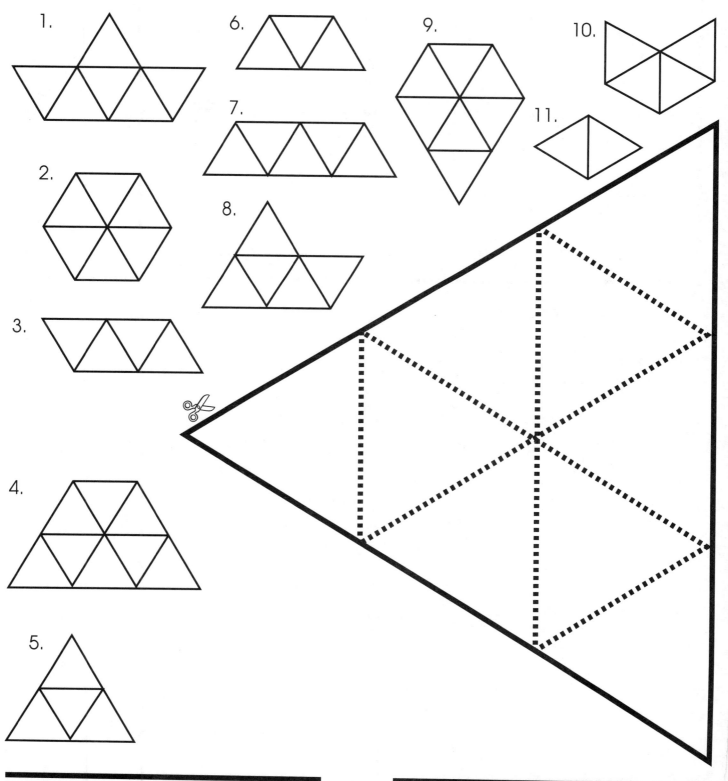

# Criss-Cross Squares Puzzle

Name_____

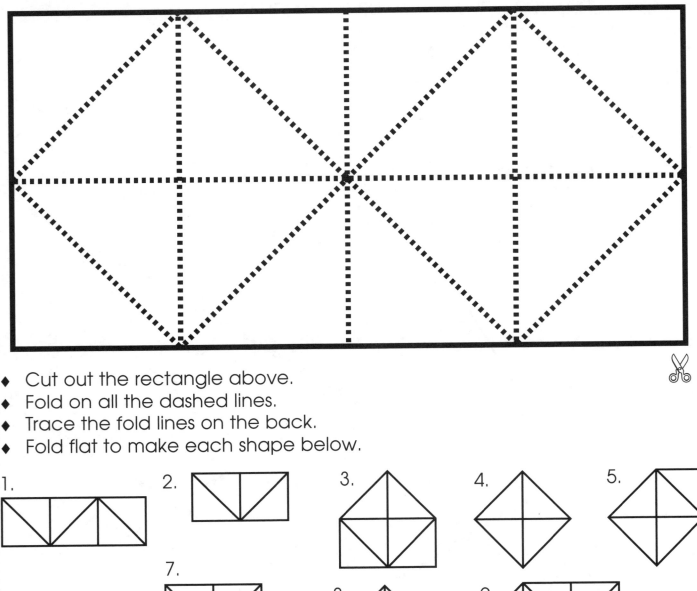

- ◆ Cut out the rectangle above.
- ◆ Fold on all the dashed lines.
- ◆ Trace the fold lines on the back.
- ◆ Fold flat to make each shape below.

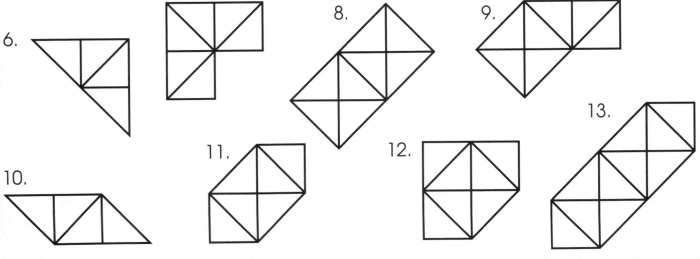

# The Weird Worm Puzzle

Name_____

- ◆ Cut out the Weird Worm.
- ◆ Fold on the dashed lines.
- ◆ Trace the fold lines on the back.
- ◆ Fold flat to make each shape below.

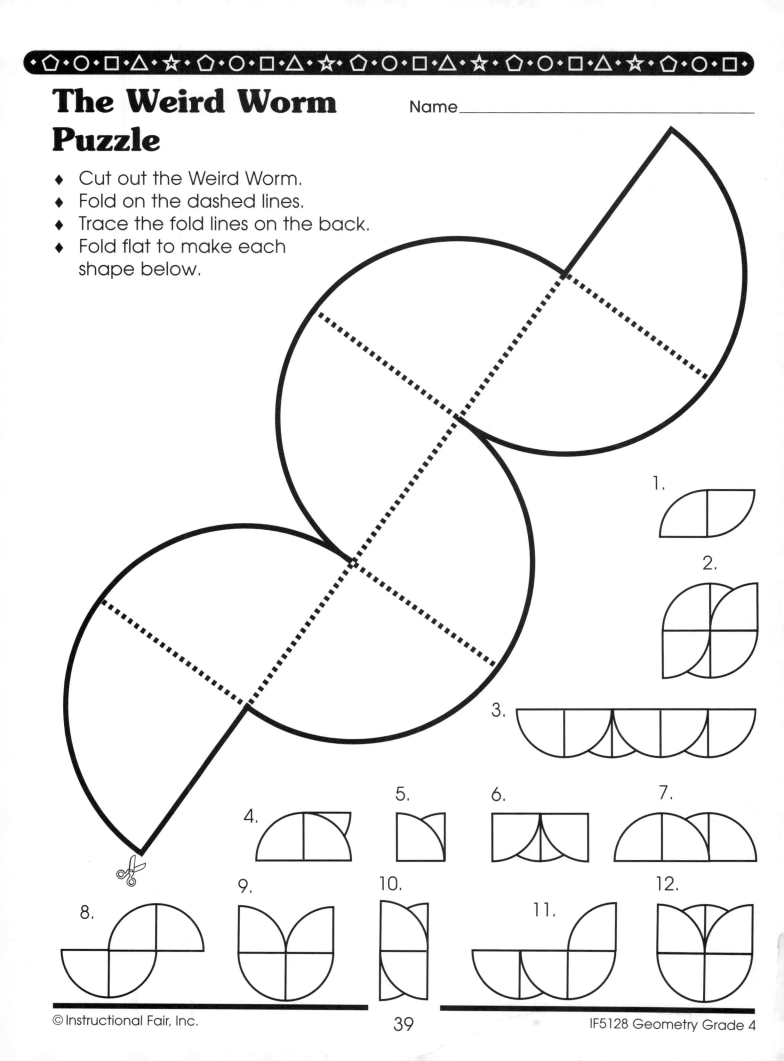

# Colorful Triangles

Name

- Cut out the rectangle below.
- Color the triangles B (blue), G (green), Y (yellow), and R (red).
- Fold on each dashed line. Copy the lines on the back.
- Color the back of each triangle the same as the front.
- Fold flat to make each design below.

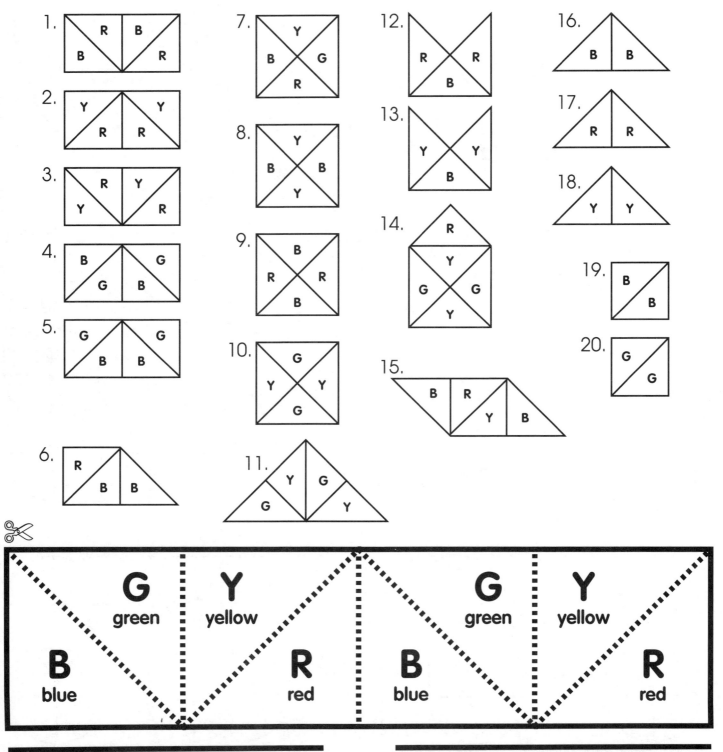

# Fold It Up!

Name _____

- ♦ Cut out the square below.
- ♦ Cut on the 4 solid lines.
- ♦ Fold on the dashed lines.
  Trace the fold lines on the back.
- ♦ Fold flat to make each shape below.

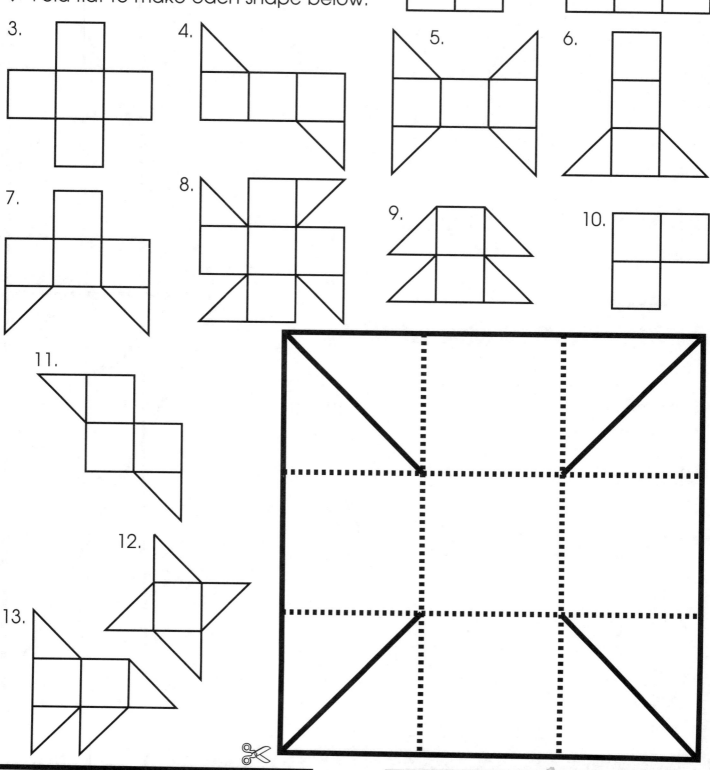

# The Folding Triangle

Name_____

- ◆ Cut out the large triangle.
- ◆ Fold on the dashed lines.
- ◆ Trace the fold lines on the back.
- ◆ Fold flat to make each shape below.

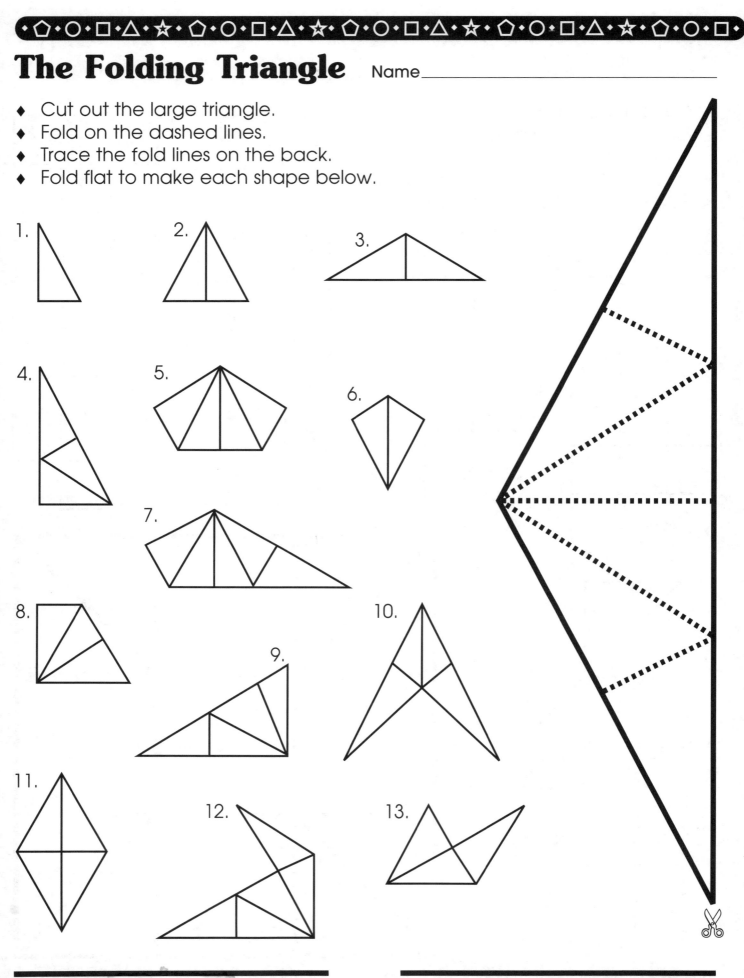

IF5128 Geometry Grade 4

# The Triangles and Squares Puzzle

Name_____

- ◆ Cut out the strip at the bottom of the page.
- ◆ Fold on the dashed lines.
- ◆ Trace the fold lines on the back.
- ◆ Fold the strip flat to make each shape below.

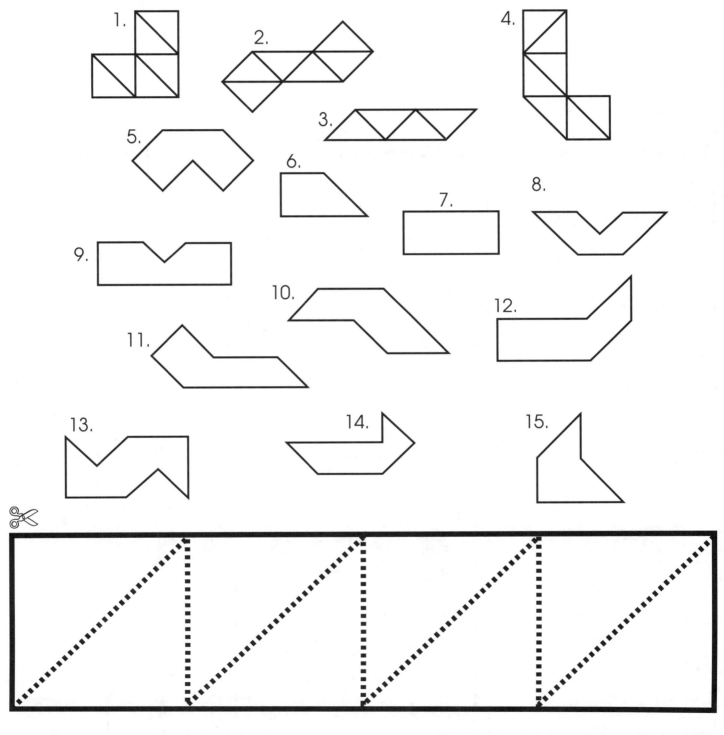

© Instructional Fair, Inc.                    IF5128 Geometry Grade 4

# ANSWER KEY
## Geometry
## Grade 4

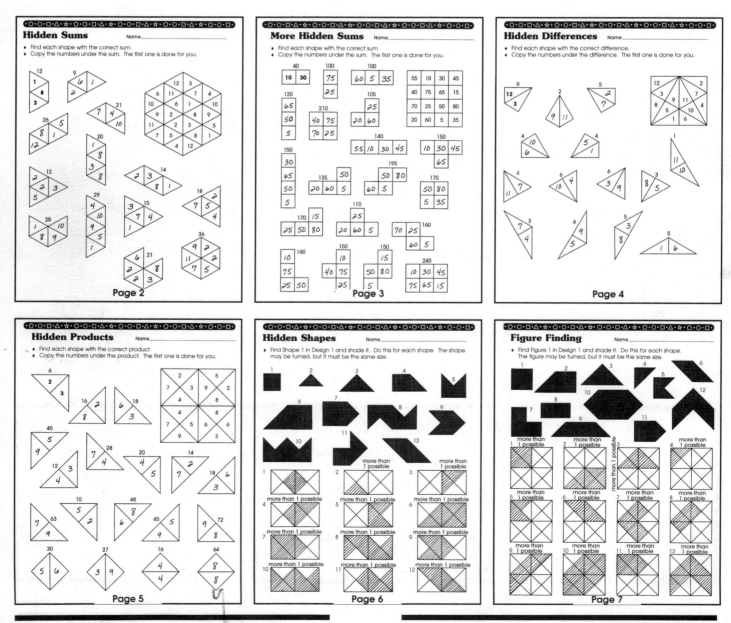

Page 2

Page 3

Page 4

Page 5

Page 6

Page 7

### Camouflaged Shapes
Name_____

♦ Find Shape 1 in Design 1 and shade it. Do this for each shape. The shape may be turned, but it must be the same size.

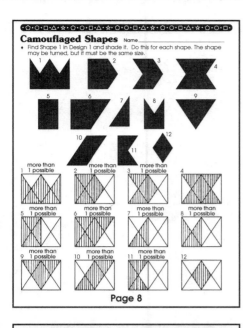

**Page 8**

### Fish in Hiding
Name_____

♦ All these fish are hiding below.
♦ Find them and shade them.

There are many possible locations for the answers.

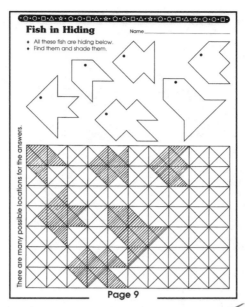

**Page 9**

### Squares and Rectangles
Name_____

♦ Connect dots in each set.
♦ Make a different square or rectangle in each set.

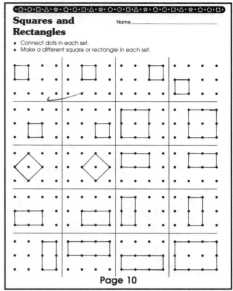

**Page 10**

### Dot Search
Name_____

♦ Connect dots to make each shape.

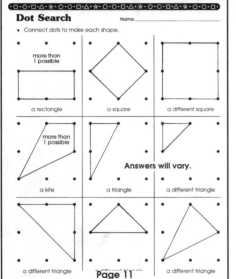

more than 1 possible
a rectangle | a square | a different square
a kite | a triangle | a different triangle
a different triangle | a different triangle | a different triangle

Answers will vary.

**Page 11**

### More Dot Search
Name_____

♦ Connect dots to make each shape.   Other answers are possible.

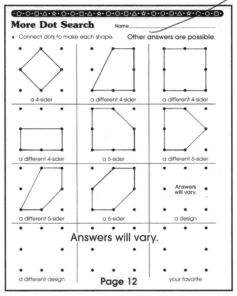

a 4-sider | a different 4-sider | a different 4-sider
a different 4-sider | a 5-sider | a different 5-sider
a different 5-sider | a 6-sider | a design

Answers will vary.

**Page 12**

### Inside Shapes
Name_____

♦ Connect dots on each circle to make each shape.

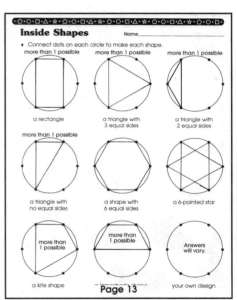

more than 1 possible | more than 1 possible | more than 1 possible
a rectangle | a triangle with 3 equal sides | a triangle with 2 equal sides
more than 1 possible
a triangle with no equal sides | a shape with 6 equal sides | a 6-pointed star
more than 1 possible | more than 1 possible
a kite shape | a lampshade shape | your own design

Answers will vary.

**Page 13**

### Connect the Dots
Name_____

♦ Connect the dots to make each shape.

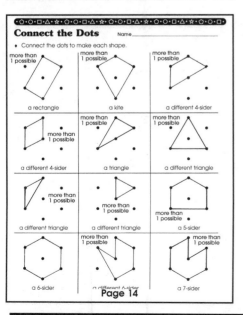

a rectangle | a kite | a different 4-sider
a different 4-sider | a triangle | a different triangle
a different triangle | a different triangle | a 5-sider
a 6-sider | a different 6-sider | a 7-sider

**Page 14**

### Shapes in Hiding
Name_____

♦ Shade triangles to make each shape.   Other answers are possible.

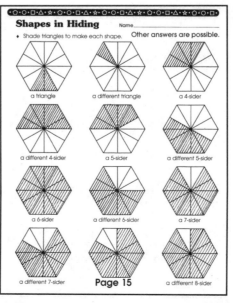

a triangle | a different triangle | a 4-sider
a different 4-sider | a 5-sider | a different 5-sider
a 6-sider | a different 6-sider | a 7-sider
a different 7-sider | a different 8-sider

**Page 15**

### The Rocket Puzzle
Name_____

♦ The rocket has 4 parts.
  Cut them apart.
♦ The rocket can change itself into many shapes.
♦ Use all 4 pieces to make each shape below.

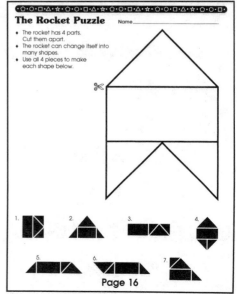

1.   2.   3.   4.

5.   6.   7.

**Page 16**

© Instructional Fair, Inc.

45

IF5128 Geometry Grade 4

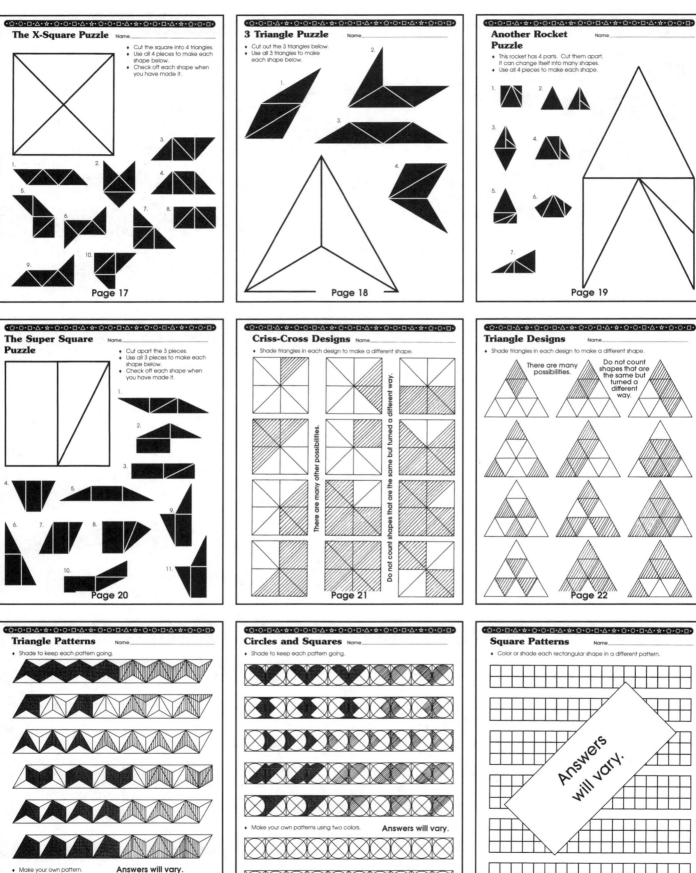

### The X-Square Puzzle

Name_____

- Cut the square into 4 triangles.
- Use all 4 pieces to make each shape below.
- Check off each shape when you have made it.

Page 17

### 3 Triangle Puzzle

Name_____

- Cut out the 3 triangles below.
- Use all 3 triangles to make each shape below.

Page 18

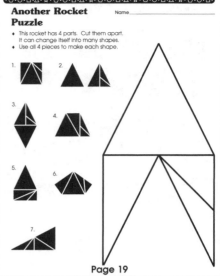

### Another Rocket Puzzle

Name_____

- This rocket has 4 parts. Cut them apart. It can change itself into many shapes.
- Use all 4 pieces to make each shape.

Page 19

### The Super Square Puzzle

Name_____

- Cut apart the 3 pieces.
- Use all 3 pieces to make each shape below.
- Check off each shape when you have made it.

Page 20

### Criss-Cross Designs

Name_____

- Shade triangles in each design to make a different shape.

There are many other possibilities.

Do not count shapes that are the same but turned a different way.

Page 21

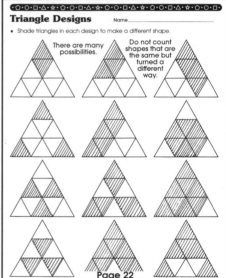

### Triangle Designs

Name_____

- Shade triangles in each design to make a different shape.

There are many possibilities.

Do not count shapes that are the same but turned a different way.

Page 22

### Triangle Patterns

Name_____

- Shade to keep each pattern going.

- Make your own pattern. **Answers will vary.**

Page 23

### Circles and Squares

Name_____

- Shade to keep each pattern going.

- Make your own patterns using two colors. **Answers will vary.**

Page 24

### Square Patterns

Name_____

- Color or shade each rectangular shape in a different pattern.

Answers will vary.

Page 25

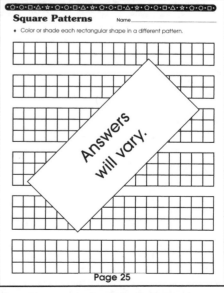

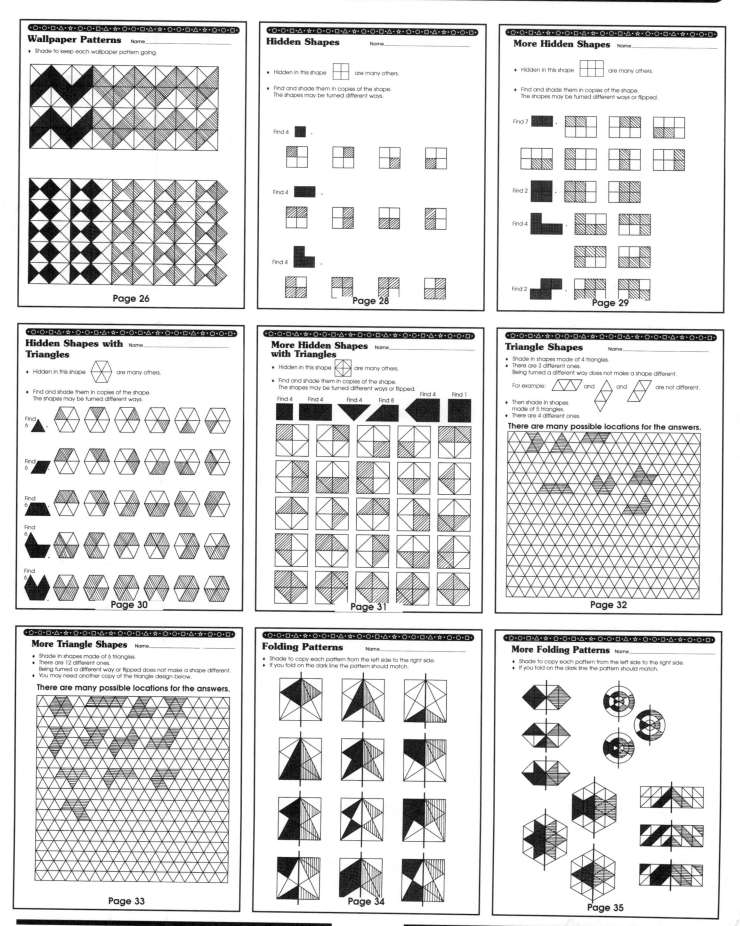

**Wallpaper Patterns** Name_____
- Shade to keep each wallpaper pattern going.

Page 26

**Hidden Shapes** Name_____
- Hidden in this shape ⬜ are many others.
- Find and shade them in copies of the shape. The shapes may be turned different ways.

Find 4 ■

Find 4 ■

Find 4 ◰

Page 28

**More Hidden Shapes** Name_____
- Hidden in this shape ⬜ are many others.
- Find and shade them in copies of the shape. The shapes may be turned different ways or flipped.

Find 7 ▦

Find 2 ▦

Find 4 ◰

Find 2 ◰

Page 29

**Hidden Shapes with Triangles** Name_____
- Hidden in this shape ⬡ are many others.
- Find and shade them in copies of the shape. The shapes may be turned different ways.

Find 6 ▲

Find 6 ◢

Find 6 ◪

Find 6 ∨

Find 6 ⋁

Page 30

**More Hidden Shapes with Triangles** Name_____
- Hidden in this shape ◰ are many others.
- Find and shade them in copies of the shape. The shapes may be turned different ways or flipped.

Find 4   Find 4   Find 4   Find 8   Find 4   Find 1

Page 31

**Triangle Shapes** Name_____
- Shade in shapes made of 4 triangles.
- There are 3 different ones. Being turned a different way does not make a shape different.

For example: ▱ and △ and ▱ are not different.

- Then shade in shapes made of 5 triangles.
- There are 4 different ones.

**There are many possible locations for the answers.**

Page 32

**More Triangle Shapes** Name_____
- Shade in shapes made of 6 triangles.
- There are 12 different ones.
  Being turned a different way or flipped does not make a shape different.
- You may need another copy of the triangle design below.

**There are many possible locations for the answers.**

Page 33

**Folding Patterns** Name_____
- Shade to copy each pattern from the left side to the right side.
- If you fold on the dark line the pattern should match.

Page 34

**More Folding Patterns** Name_____
- Shade to copy each pattern from the left side to the right side.
- If you fold on the dark line the pattern should match.

Page 35

47

IF5128 Geometry Grade 4

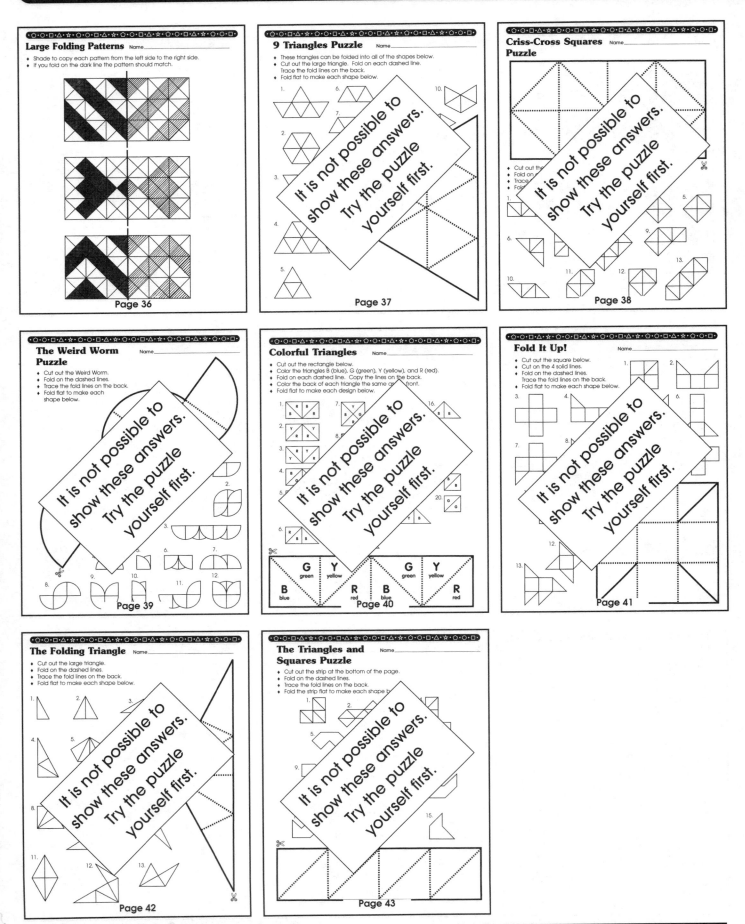

**Large Folding Patterns** Name_____

♦ Shade to copy each pattern from the left side to the right side.
♦ If you fold on the dark line the pattern should match.

Page 36

**9 Triangles Puzzle** Name_____

♦ These triangles can be folded into all of the shapes below.
♦ Cut out the large triangle. Fold on each dashed line. Trace the fold lines on the back.
♦ Fold flat to make each shape below.

It is not possible to show these answers. Try the puzzle yourself first.

Page 37

**Criss-Cross Squares Puzzle** Name_____

♦ Cut out the
♦ Fold on
♦ Trace
♦ Fold

It is not possible to show these answers. Try the puzzle yourself first.

Page 38

**The Weird Worm Puzzle** Name_____

♦ Cut out the Weird Worm.
♦ Fold on the dashed lines.
♦ Trace the fold lines on the back.
♦ Fold flat to make each shape below.

It is not possible to show these answers. Try the puzzle yourself first.

Page 39

**Colorful Triangles** Name_____

♦ Cut out the rectangle below.
♦ Color the triangles B (blue), G (green), Y (yellow), and R (red).
♦ Fold on each dashed line. Copy the lines on the back.
♦ Color the back of each triangle the same as front.
♦ Fold flat to make each design below.

It is not possible to show these answers. Try the puzzle yourself first.

| G | Y | | G | Y |
| green | yellow | | green | yellow |
| B | R | | B | R |
| blue | red | | blue | red |

Page 40

**Fold It Up!** Name_____

♦ Cut out the square below.
♦ Cut on the 4 solid lines.
♦ Fold on the dashed lines. Trace the fold lines on the back.
♦ Fold flat to make each shape below.

It is not possible to show these answers. Try the puzzle yourself first.

Page 41

**The Folding Triangle** Name_____

♦ Cut out the large triangle.
♦ Fold on the dashed lines.
♦ Trace the fold lines on the back.
♦ Fold flat to make each shape below.

It is not possible to show these answers. Try the puzzle yourself first.

Page 42

**The Triangles and Squares Puzzle** Name_____

♦ Cut out the strip at the bottom of the page.
♦ Fold on the dashed lines.
♦ Trace the fold lines on the back.
♦ Fold the strip flat to make each shape

It is not possible to show these answers. Try the puzzle yourself first.

Page 43

IF5128 Geometry Grade 4